Let's take a trip, just you and me
We'll follow the route from A to Zee
Imagine the fun and the things we'll see
In Barbie Town – it's the place to be!

sugar Shoppe

Ballet studio

chic Boutique

Theatre

Barbie!

Valet

tique

£6.99
UK only

Barbie

Where it's at!

"Hi girls! Here it is! The coolest, trendiest Barbie Annual ever!"

POW!

Prepare for a blast of energy!
Check out everything that's bright and new
with Barbie and her friends in 70 pages of stories and action, puzzles and games
and things to make and do.
Step into Barbie Town –
it's where fashion and fantasy meet and where dreams and wishes come true!

This Barbie Annual 2004 belongs to:

_____

_____

2

Written by Jane Clempner
Designed by Sheryl Bone

Edited by Brenda Apsley and Jane Clempner
Published in Great Britain in 2003
by Egmont Books Limited,
239 Kensington High Street, London, W8 6SA.
Printed in Italy   ISBN: 0 7498 5847 8

Where it's at!

PROJECT BARBIE

Page 6   Story: SOS!
Page 14   Puzzle Fun
Page 18   Colouring

PEACE, LOVE, BARBIE

Page 20   Story: Groovy Baby!
Page 28   Colouring
Page 30   Puzzle Fun
Page 34   Make: Paper Flowers

DAZZLE AND DANCE

Page 36   Story: The Magic Fan
Page 44   Colouring
Page 46   Puzzle Fun
Page 48   Make: A Fan

MY SPECIAL THINGS

Page 50   Game: Let's Go Shopping!
Page 52   Puzzle Fun
Page 54   Quiz: What's Your Style?

SWEET SURPRISE

Page 56   Make: Chocolate Crunch
Page 57   Make: Sugar Shoppe Truffles
Page 58   Make: A Sweet Surprise!
Page 59   Puzzle Fun

GLAMOROUS BARBIE

Page 60   Colouring

FANTASY BARBIE

Page 62   Story: The Dream Dance
Page 68   Quiz: Discover Your Dream!
Page 69   Colouring

"Go for it girls!
Reach for romance
and adventure!
And may your dreams
come true in 2004!"

Barbie x

SOS!

At Barbie Town School, the bell for lessons rang.

"It's science – again," moaned Christie, as Barbie and her friends pulled on their white lab coats.

"Too difficult for your little brains?" sneered Josie Jones, pushing her way to the front of the line. "Better stick to shopping – it's what you're good at!"

"Take no notice," urged Barbie, leading her friends to their seats. "She likes to cause trouble."

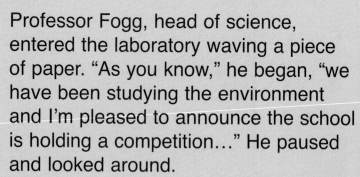

Professor Fogg, head of science, entered the laboratory waving a piece of paper. "As you know," he began, "we have been studying the environment and I'm pleased to announce the school is holding a competition…" He paused and looked around.

"Sounds exciting!" beamed Josie Jones.

"Your mission," he looked back at his notes, "is to design a project to show how science can help us to be more environmentally friendly in our everyday lives."

Josie Jones began scribbling ideas in her notebook.

"You have four weeks to complete your project and, thanks to the generosity of our headmistress, the winner will have the honour of opening our new science block, and receive prize money of £100! Oh, and her entire class has a day's holiday."

"Now you're talking!" cheered Christie.

During the next four weeks the school labs were in constant use. Barbie popped her head around the door several times and saw groups of girls huddled around their projects. Josie Jones was usually one of them.

"Come to steal our ideas?" she sneered when she spotted Barbie. "Can't think of any of your own?"

"Oh, I'd so like to win this," said Barbie to Christie, later. "That would show her!"

"But you don't have a project!" pointed out Teresa.

"I'm… thinking!" said Barbie.

But the truth was, she hadn't thought of a single idea, and by the final weekend she was in a panic. She sent a frantic text message to all her friends:

@SS ·SOS

Within minutes, Barbie's friends had gathered outside their favourite place – the Sugar Shoppe. "What's the matter?" asked Kira. "SOS means major distress!"

"Too right," said Barbie. "I have a serious problem! I have to choose between science – and shopping!"

"You're not still thinking about that science project?" asked Christie. "The deadline is Monday!"

"Exactly!" exclaimed Barbie. "I really need to spend the weekend at the labs, but I've also been invited to the Theatre tomorrow and I really don't have a thing to wear, so I really have to go shopping!"

"We'll toss a coin!" suggested Teresa. But at that moment, Josie Jones walked by. "Hey girls, it's Saturday. Shouldn't you be at Chic Boutique? I hear there's a sale on!"

That did it! Barbie and her friends headed straight for the school labs!

Everyone else had finished their projects and packed away, so they had the place to themselves.

"Thinking caps on!" ordered Barbie.

The girls sat at a high bench with notebooks and pens. Ten minutes passed.

"I know!" said Teresa, breaking the silence. "Let's invent a clock that speeds up during lessons and slows down during break-time!"

"Be serious!" chuckled Barbie.

"How about a shopping bag that you can fill and fill but never gets any heavier?" suggested Christie.

"I wish!" laughed Barbie. "But it doesn't really help the environment!"

"How about a solar powered mobile phone?" suggested Kira. "Or X-ray specs to see into people's houses so you know when they leave lights on or waste water?"

The girls had lots of fun, but after an hour their pages were still blank.

"Hey, look at this," said Christie, scooping a crumpled magazine page from beneath her seat. She read it out to the others: "Robo-dog – the amazing robotic pet that recycles all your household waste. A must for every home at just £49.99!"

"All the best ideas are taken!" sighed Barbie.

"Come on, let's go home."

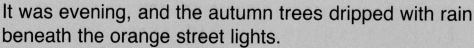

It was evening, and the autumn trees dripped with rain beneath the orange street lights.

"Nature does a pretty neat job of recycling," said Teresa, shuffling through the damp carpet of colourful leaves.

"But look at all the ugly dustbins," said Kira. "We humans make so much rubbish!"

Barbie agreed. "We have too much... stuff! Take my night out tomorrow. I have lots of clothes already, but I still want a new outfit to wear!"

"Borrow my pink skirt," suggested Teresa.

"And my new jacket," offered Kira.

"Really? Oh, that would be... hang on! Oooo I love you!" Barbie began jumping excitedly on the spot. "You've given me the best idea ever!" She ran back towards the school and that was the last her friends saw of her until Monday morning!

Barbie marched into the Great Hall carrying her science project in a Chic Boutique shopping bag!

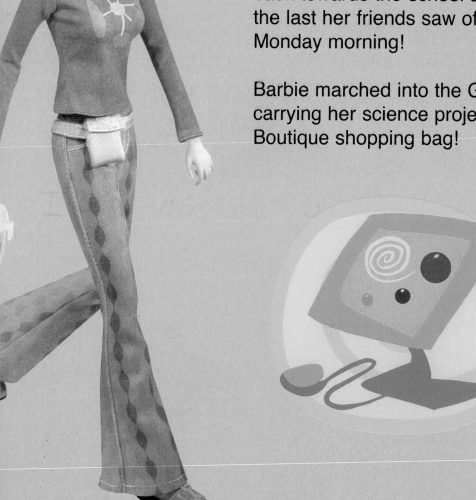

The room echoed with excited chatter as all kinds of inventions were displayed on the tables. Josie Jones was at the table next to Barbie. A loud bell rang and the judges came in. A hush fell. Barbie was on table number 1.

"May we see?" asked the first judge, pointing at her shopping bag. Barbie lifted the bag and Josie Jones let out a spluttering laugh. "It's a computer!" she giggled. "I hate to tell you, Barbie, but I think someone's already invented that!" "It's not the computer," said Barbie, crossly. "It's what's on the screen!" She turned it to show the judges. "I call it SOS, which stands for Swap Over Shop. It's a new website for girls. We swap and share clothes, accessories and ideas, so it's like recycling! It means we spend less time and energy shopping and we save on waste and resources."

The second judge perched his spectacles on top of his head and peered at the screen. "I see," he said, and scribbled something on his list. "Now, moving on. Miss Jones, may we see your project?"

Josie stood aside and Barbie gasped. It was a robotic cat, just like the dog they had seen in the magazine ad! "I've designed a remote controlled cat to recycle household waste," said Josie, proudly.
"Indeed!" The judge was clearly impressed.

"Rather like this?" interrupted Christie, stepping up and pulling the crumpled page from her pocket.
There was a long silence. Josie turned bright red and the judge took a pen from his top pocket. He wrote a word next to Josie's name on his list: Disqualified.

12

At the opening of the smart new school science block, Professor Fogg stood poised. "And now we ask the winner of our science competition to officially open our new labs."
Barbie stepped up and cut the ribbon to a huge round of applause. "Three cheers for Barbie – and a whole day off school!" said Christie.

"I have something I want to give to the school," said Barbie, handing a large box to Professor Fogg. "It's Robo-dog. I bought it with some of my prize money."
"And what are you planning to do with the rest?" the happy professor asked.
Barbie stepped down and stood with her friends. "That's easy. Go shopping – of course!"

13

You can... work it out

Use this code to read Barbie's message:

I t as c o o l t o

b e s m a r t

12

"I use this code to send secret messages to my friends."

Which two of these robotic pets are identical?

a

b

c

d

e

f

"Recycling is pretty smart!"

Answer: a and e

You can... work it out

Here are some strange sums. Some numbers have been replaced by pictures. Can you work out what number each picture represents?

9 - 2 = ✱

♥ - ✱ = ✿

✱ + ✦ = 11

✿ + ✿ = 👗

✦ + 🌀 = 9

👗 + 🧦 = ♥

7 - ✦ = ♥

4 + ♥ - 🧦 = 🧦

♥ + 🌀 = ♥

🌀 - ♥ + ✦ = 🧦

16

"Doing sums is easy! Especially when you can check out the answers below!"

Barbie has her very own PINK computer!
Can you show her which wire connects her to it?

a

b

c

d

You can... work it out

17

"That's a MAZE ing!"

You can... colour in!

18

"Barbie and Christie are best friends. Today they are going shopping together. Use your crayons or pens to help them look their best."

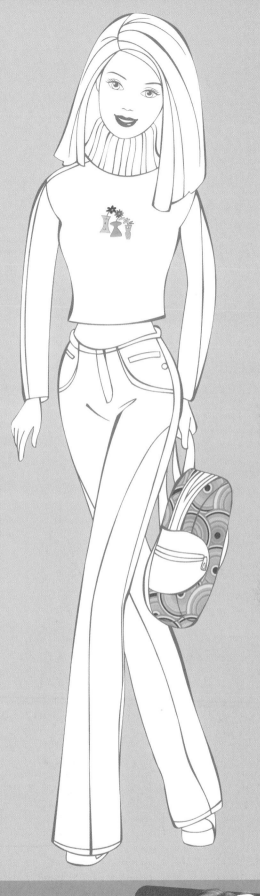

19

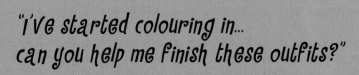
"I've started colouring in...
can you help me finish these outfits?"

You can... read it!

Groovy Baby!

Barbie couldn't wait to tell her friends about the movie she had just seen.
"It was set in the 1960's," she told Teresa and Kira, as they drove out to Barbie Town Lake one Sunday afternoon. "People were really hip and cool and cared about world peace and love. They wore flowers in their hair and walked around with bare feet."
"Not if they were out here," said Kira, stepping out of the car into a muddy puddle!

"Everything was more wholesome then," Barbie continued, taking the picnic basket from the boot. "So I've made today's picnic entirely from organic vegetables!"

Kira took the basket with a horrified look. "What – no truffles and fudge from the Sugar Shoppe?"

"No, and I've brought my guitar." Barbie pulled the battered-looking instrument from the car and her friends exchanged a worried look. "I've been writing songs," she continued, "to teach people about peace and love. I'll sing them to you!" And she marched off towards the Lake.

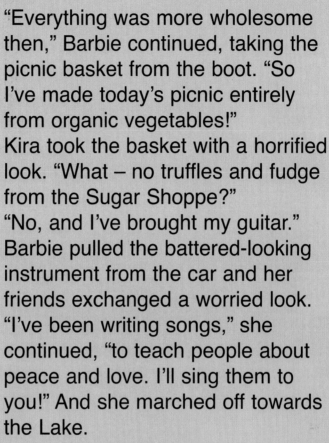

That was just the beginning! The following Sunday when Barbie arrived to collect her friends they could hardly believe their eyes. Barbie's car was now fluorescent pink and decorated with huge swirly flowers. She stepped out wearing plaits, swirls and some very hippy accessories! "I've been working on my songs," she chirped. "Peace and love mean everything… Oh, I can teach the world to sing…"
"Let's go!" said Kira, jumping into the passenger seat with her fingers in her ears. "And please don't sing at the Lake – the ducks are sensitive at this time of year!"
"Very funny," said Barbie, driving off and continuing with the first verse:
"Fill your day with pretty flowers… and love will come in silver showers… Do you like it? I've spent ages on it. And guess what! A TV channel is coming to Barbie Town next month to stage a talent show. I'm going to enter!" Her friends exchanged a look.

They met up later that day.
"What are we going to do?" said Kira. "She's our friend. We should tell her she can't sing!"
"And her songs are terrible!" agreed Teresa. "But I'm not telling her!"
Kira shrugged. "Well, if we don't, who will?"

22

The next day at school Barbie was filling in her application form for the talent show. "I've changed my name to Daisy May Peacelove," she announced. "Do you like it?"
"Are you serious?" asked Kira.
Barbie looked shocked. "Of course I'm serious. This could be my big break!"
She put the application form into its envelope.
"Here, let me take that," said Teresa. "I'm… um… going to the post box at break time. I'll post it for you."
"Thanks!" said Barbie, handing over the envelope and heading off, humming.
"Now what are you going to do?" asked Kira.
"Lose it... forget to post it... my dog's going to eat it! Anything to stop Barbie going on stage and making a fool of herself in front of millions!"

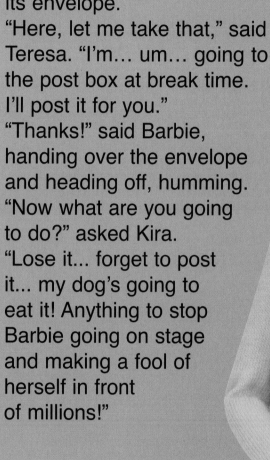

23

As the day of the talent show approached, Kira and Teresa began to feel guilty. "Barbie will be so disappointed when she finds they never received her application. She'll hate us!" moaned Teresa.

"We had no choice," said Kira. "It was our duty, as friends."

"Hey, you two! You're always whispering these days!" Barbie came bounding up. "I'm so excited! Only a week to go! I've re-written the chorus to my second song. You want to hear it?"

"Um… not now," mumbled Kira. "Homework to do."

"Never mind. See you at the show. Be sure to sit in the front row. I won't forget you when I'm famous!"

Groovy Baby!

Exactly one week later, Teresa and Kira filed nervously into Barbie Town Theatre beneath a huge banner saying: STAR SEARCH 2004! Inside there was a buzz of anticipation. The TV cameras were in position and bright spotlights focused on the stage.

"Have you seen Barbie lately?" whispered Teresa, settling into her front row seat.

"No, not at all. I've been avoiding her. I feel so bad!" Just then the theatre lights dimmed and the drums rolled. The girls joined in the applause as the curtains parted and the first act nervously took to the stage. His name was Will and he was the school heart-throb! His performance was amazing and everyone began to relax and enjoy the show.

After two hours the last act left the stage and the judges had to make their decision. Then the drums rolled again and a voice made an announcement:

"Please give a warm welcome to the person who made this show possible, the organizer of Star Search 2004… Barbie!"

25

You can... read it!

Teresa and Kira sat frozen in their seats.
Barbie walked glamorously onto the stage and took her
place at the microphone. "My thanks to Central TV for
holding such a wonderful show here in Barbie Town,"
she said, smiling and confident. "And congratulations
to all the fabulous new talent we have seen tonight."
The audience clapped.
"I'm pleased to announce that the winner of
Star Search 2004 is an incredible
singer/songwriter who is sure to go far
– Will Plumber!"
Will walked on stage. Barbie kissed
him and handed him his award.

When the crowds had left, Teresa
and Kira crept backstage and
found the dressing rooms.
"Come and give me a hug!" said
Barbie, leaping up as they came
in. "I'm sorry I played a trick on
you, but your faces were so
funny when I started singing.
I know my songs were terrible.
I was never really going to
enter. I was just teasing!"

Groovy Baby!

Her friends weren't sure whether to laugh or cry! "I haven't seen you much lately because I've been so busy organizing this show. And guess what, Central TV have asked me to do more presenting for them."

"So it was your big break, after all!" smiled Kira, hugging her friend.

"And you got to kiss Will Plumber!" said Teresa. "I'm so jealous. You're the best!"

"I'm not the best at everything!" laughed Barbie. "But I do have the best friends – ever!" And that night in Barbie Town there was plenty of peace and love to go round.

27

You can... colour it!

"Do you like Barbie's new look? Choose colours to make her really groovy!"

Spot the difference!

29

"There are 10 differences between these two pictures. When you have found them, colour the two girls to make them look as different as possible!"

Here are some of Barbie's favourite 'Peace and Love' badges. Use your crayons or pens to colour them in, then design some of your own!

You can... work it out!

30

"Groovy baby!"

Join these pretty flowers into matching pairs.
Which is the odd one out?

You can... work it out!

Odd
One Out!

31

"I love all flowers, but my favourite has to
be the rose. What's yours?"

How many butterflies can you count?
Join the dots to see why there are so many!

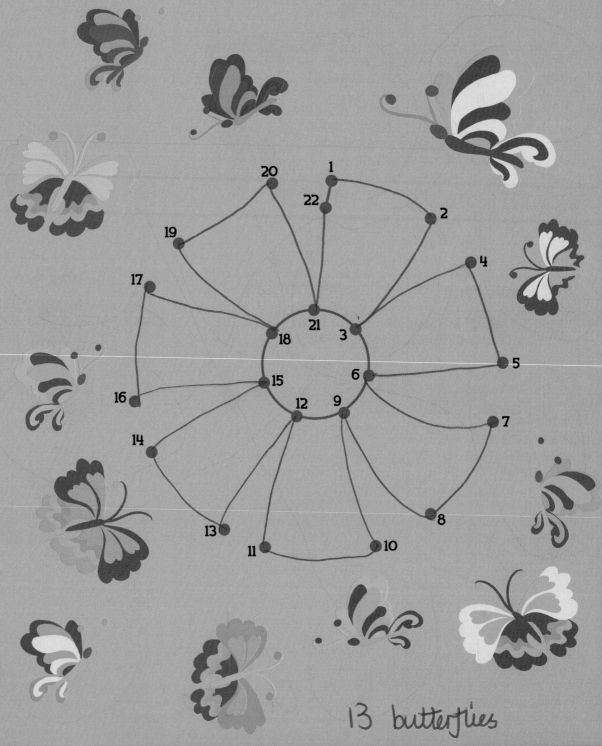

13 butterflies

"Flower power!"

Can you join these words together to find the names of some garden flowers?

SNOW

BLUE

BUTTER

SNAP

GLOVE

GYPSY

PEA

DRAGON

GRASS

SWEET

FOX

SUN

DROP

BELL

FLOWER

CUP

"Flowers have such pretty names. Do you know anyone with a flower for their name?"

You can... make it!

Paper Flowers

You will need:

Coloured crepe paper – pink, green, yellow, red
Thin wire cut into lengths for the stems
Scissors
Glue

1. Cut a small strip of crepe paper and make frills along one side.

3. Cut 6 – 8 petals from the crepe paper using the template on this page as a guide.

template

2. Glue this around the end of a piece of wire to make a centre for your flower.

Glue

4. One by one, glue your petals around the centrepiece. Now make more flowers in the same way.

32

"Make beautiful flowers that will last all year!"

Use this template to make a different kind of flower.

template

5. Cut the complete shape from crepe paper and wrap it around your centrepiece – make sure the smaller petals are at the centre. Bend out the petals as you go. You can experiment with different shapes and sizes of petals.

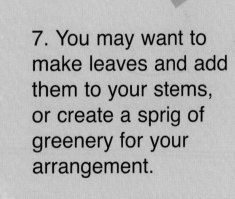

6. Cut long strips of green paper to wrap around the stems. Secure with glue.

7. You may want to make leaves and add them to your stems, or create a sprig of greenery for your arrangement.

35

"Arrange your flowers in a vase for everyone to admire!"

The Magic Fan

Barbie met Ella and Izzy at the Ballet Studio. They slipped into their pink leotards and laced their ribbons. They tied each other's hair into a bun with pins and hair spray. It took ages! Madame Lujenco wouldn't allow you to dance with a hair out of place!

Ballet classes weren't easy! Madame Lujenco was very strict.
"Turn out your legs, stretch and point! We're not here for fun!" she would say, banging her stick and making the floorboards rattle. "To be a dancer takes hard work!"

"I wonder what she was like when she was young," Barbie whispered to Ella. "She's so old!"
"Her fingers are all crooked," agreed Ella.
"Maybe she was once a real ballerina," added Izzy.

Barbie was a good dancer, but she wanted to be the best. As Madame would say, only the best is good enough. Barbie knew there was a show coming up – a proper ballet. She dreamed of being chosen to take the lead. So far she had only made it into the chorus. But one evening, everything changed…

"Straight backs. Tummies in. Chassez!" Madame Lujenco clapped her hands. "That's enough for now girls. Gather round. The time has come to select the dancers who will star in our next ballet at Barbie Town Theatre."

There was an excited gasp.

"In order to choose, I must teach you a new dance. It is for the finale of the ballet. It's called the Tarantella."

Barbie and her friends exchanged a puzzled glance.

"This is a dance of passion, unlike anything I have taught you before. Some of you," she said, looking around the class, "may find it hard. Impossible even. But we will practise. And then I will decide."

37

Barbie learnt the steps easily. So did Ella and Izzy. But the music was very fast. And the girls had to wear long skirts and shoes with heels. And they had to carry a fan. Putting it all together was hard.

Barbie practised at home every night the following week. But no matter how she tried, she knew it wasn't quite right. She wasn't looking forward to her next class. In the studio, Ella and Izzy danced first. They seemed to have picked it up so easily. Then it was Barbie's turn. She stood in position. Madame Lujenco watched closely. The music began. Barbie took a few steps, then stopped. "It's not right," she said, bowing her head and dropping her fan. She could feel tears welling up. "I can't do it." And she ran from the studio.

Madame Lujenco followed her in to the changing room. "This is wonderful," she said, handing Barbie a tissue. "This shows me you understand the dance. You know what it takes to be danced properly."
Barbie dried her eyes.
"Here, I want you to have something," said Madame Lujenco, handing Barbie an old box. "I carried this when I danced the Tarantella many years ago. It is very precious."
Barbie lifted the lid and saw the most exquisite fan she had ever seen. It was made of lace and it sparkled with jewels.
"You may borrow it, to practise. Then… we will see!"

40

Barbie waited until everyone had gone home and the Ballet Studio was silent. She wanted to practise with the fan.

The caretaker came in to switch the lights off. Barbie told him she had permission to stay late. It was only a little white lie.

She started the music and took the fan from its box. It opened with a flick of her wrist, its bright colours dazzling her eyes. Her feet knew the steps. They moved in time with the music. Faster and faster, she twisted and twirled, her skirt billowing around her, her heels tapping on the floorboards, faster and louder, until the room began to spin and suddenly, everything went black...

Barbie woke to feel her face being
gently fanned.
"Are you OK?" said a kind voice.
"I think you fainted!"
Barbie blinked.
"Hi! I'm Danny. I dance here sometimes."
Barbie sat up. He was terribly tall
and handsome and she suddenly felt
embarrassed. "I… I was just practising."
"The Tarantella?" he asked, picking up the
fan and handing it back to her.
"Yes."
"Then let me help you." He lifted her to her
feet and the music started. He led her to the
back of the studio, placed an arm around her
waist and they began to dance.

They danced and danced until the sky
outside grew dark and it was time for him to
leave. At the Studio door he turned and
took Barbie's hand. "You dance like a
prima ballerina," he said. "One day I will
see you dance on stage. And one day we
will dance together again."
That night, Barbie walked home beneath
the Barbie Town stars with wings on
her feet.

41

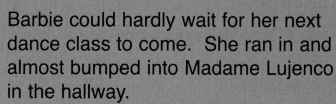

Barbie could hardly wait for her next dance class to come. She ran in and almost bumped into Madame Lujenco in the hallway.

"You're in a hurry, young lady!"

"Yes… I just wanted to give you back the fan. I've been practising. I think I can do it now!"

"Has the fan worked its magic, do you think?"

"Magic?"

"Oh yes," said the teacher, taking it from Barbie. "When I danced with this fan on stage, a young man in the audience fell in love with me. We have been married for forty years this July!"

"Oh!" Barbie stared at her. "That is the magic! Now come. Show me if all your practising has been worthwhile!"

The Magic Fan

Barbie danced in front of the class and when she had finished, everyone clapped. She thought she saw Madame Lujenco wipe a tear from her eye.
"Barbie has shown us how the Tarantella should be danced," she said. "And that is why I am choosing her to take the lead in our next ballet."
Barbie had never felt so happy. She would be dancing on stage, in Barbie Town Theatre, just like a real ballerina. And she couldn't help wondering who might be watching…

43

You can... colour it!

42

"Dancing is one of my favourite things. What's yours?"

You can... colour it!

45

"Copy colour Barbie and her friends at their dance class."

Unscramble the letters to find some other kinds of dance:

OCLFANME

ARMUB — Rumba

PTA — Tap

VEJI — Jive

ZLWTA — Waltz

MBSAA — Samba

You can... work it out

46

"Barbie and her friends love to dance! At the Ballet Studio in Barbie Town there are all kinds of dance lessons, from Ballet to Bebop!"

Match the dancers to their shadows.

a   b   c   d   e

1   2   3   4   5

You can... work it out

47

"Dancing is a great way to keep fit, have fun and make new friends!"

Answers: a3, b5, c2, d4, e1

A Fan

You will need:

A3 sheet of white or coloured paper
White, silver or gold paper doily
Matching cake frill
Curling ribbon
Pencil
Ruler
Scissors
Glue
Stapler or sticky tape

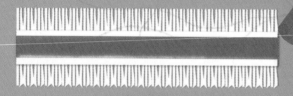

1. Cut your sheet of
    paper to size by
    measuring and cutting
    a 9mm strip from
    the top.

2. Cut your paper doily
    into quarters.

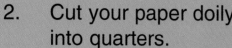

"Make a beautiful fan, just like Barbie's!"

3. Glue the four pieces of doily to the top of your piece of paper to make a frill. Allow to dry.

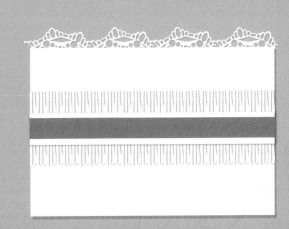

4. Turn your paper over. This will be the front of your fan.

5. Cut your cake frill to the same length as your paper and glue across the front. Allow to dry.

6. Carefully fold your fan into a concertina and hold one end in place with staples or sticky tape.

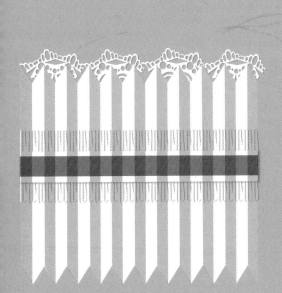

7. Add a bow and two 'tails' of curling ribbon.

"You may want to add extra sparkles to your fan with glitter or sequins!"

You can... make it!

Let's Go Shopping!

Join Barbie and her friends at Barbie Town's shopping hotspot – Chic Boutique!

You can have fun playing this game with your friends, or by yourself.

You stop to try on shoes **miss a go**

You spot a bargain **move ahead 2 spaces**

You find the outfit of your dreams **have an extra go**

You lose your credit card **go back to the beginning!**

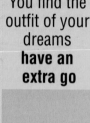

You wait while your bouquet is made **miss a go**

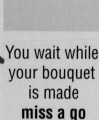

You discover a new department **have an extra go**

Way In

50

"Everything a girl needs can be found at Chic Boutique! Whether it's a trendy new outfit, some beautiful flowers or a tasty snack."

You stop for
a snack
miss a go

Your shopping
bags break –
**move back
5 spaces**

You stop for
a drink
miss a go

You find
the lifts
**move ahead
3 spaces**

You can't
decide which
outfit you
like best
miss a go

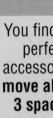

Your shopping
is too heavy
**move back
3 spaces**

You find the
perfect
accessories
**move ahead
3 spaces**

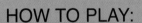

You can... play it!

HOW TO PLAY:

First, decide who you want to be!
Barbie, Teresa, Christie and Ella ALL
love shopping!
Cut carefully around the dotted lines to
create your characters. Find a dice.
Put your characters on the Way In.
Roll the dice and follow the path around
Chic Boutique, following any instructions
you land on. Whoever reaches the Way
Out first is the winner!

51

"Chic Boutique is full of special things."

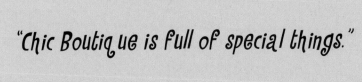

You can... work it out!

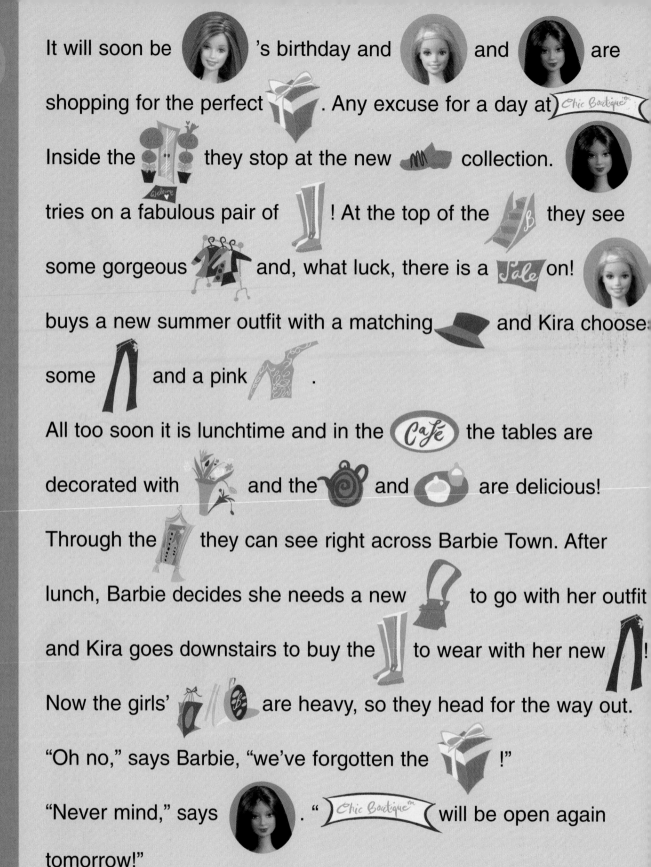

It will soon be [Barbie]'s birthday and [Barbie] and [Barbie] are shopping for the perfect [present]. Any excuse for a day at *Chic Boutique*!

Inside the [shop] they stop at the new [shoes] collection. [Barbie] tries on a fabulous pair of [boots]! At the top of the [escalator] they see some gorgeous [clothes] and, what luck, there is a *Sale* on! [Barbie] buys a new summer outfit with a matching [hat] and Kira chooses some [trousers] and a pink [top].

All too soon it is lunchtime and in the *Café* the tables are decorated with [flowers] and the [tea] and [cakes] are delicious! Through the [window] they can see right across Barbie Town. After lunch, Barbie decides she needs a new [bag] to go with her outfit and Kira goes downstairs to buy the [boots] to wear with her new [trousers]!

Now the girls' [bags] are heavy, so they head for the way out. "Oh no," says Barbie, "we've forgotten the [present]!"

"Never mind," says [Barbie]. "*Chic Boutique* will be open again tomorrow!"

"Read the story using the pictures to help you."

52

There are so many shoes in the shoe department.
Can you match them into pairs?

You can... work it out!

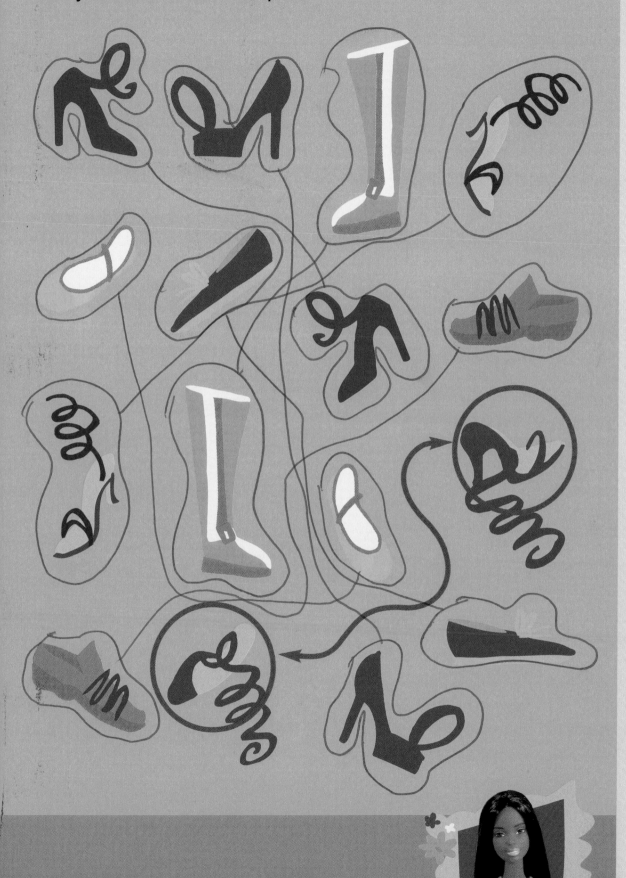

53

"Which shoes do you like best?"

you can... discover it!

What's Your Style?

Have fun with this quiz to find out what your clothes say about YOU!

Here are 11 questions. You choose an answer – a, b, c or d. At the end, add up which letter you have scored most often and find out what your answers mean.

1. If you could redecorate your bedroom, which colour would you choose?
a Lavender
b White
c Blue
d Pink

2. You are going shopping. Which type of footwear do you wear?
a Sensible shoes
b Boots
c Comfy trainers
d High heels

3. It's snowing and you are off for a walk. What do you put on?
a A warm anorak
b Anything with a designer label
c Matching scarf, hat and gloves
d Something furry

4. If you could take one thing to a desert island, which would it be?
a Your computer
b Your designer sunglasses
c Your CD player
d Your make-up bag

5. Which hairstyle do you wear most often?
a Short and sleek
b You change too often to say
c A ponytail to keep it out of the way
d Long and loose

Mostly a's: Smarty Pants
You're one sharp cookie! Ambitious and bright, your no-nonsense approach to clothes shows that you mean business. You always look immaculate and hope that your smart appearance will impress others – but be careful not to come across as cold and unapproachable. Try relaxing a little!

Mostly b's: Designer Babe
Too cool for words! You are hip, hot and happening! You love shopping, fashion magazines – and more shopping! You dress to be noticed and prefer designer labels. You dream of being on the catwal yourself. Try not to follow every new tren but develop your own style – you don't want to become a fashion victim!

6. **Which is your ideal way to spend a Saturday?**
   a Reading or travelling
   b Shopping with friends or by yourself
   c Playing sport then watching a movie
   d At a party with your friends

7. **Which of these most closely describes your nails?**
   a Short, neat and polished
   b Always perfect with a French manicure
   c You only wear nail varnish for special occasions
   d Your toes and fingernails always match and are usually sparkly!

8. **Which kind of bag are you most likely to be carrying?**
   a A briefcase that keeps all your important belongings safe
   b A small designer handbag to carry your phone and your credit card
   c A sporty holdall or backpack that fits everything in
   d Whatever matches your outfit – you have so many!

9. **Which of the following best describes your wardrobe?**
   a Well organized with lots of dark colours and smart separates
   b It never stays the same as you have a clear out every season
   c You keep your clothes in drawers more than a wardrobe
   d It's an Aladdin's cave – packed with pink sparkly things

10. **How many pairs of trainers do you own?**
    a None – they are too scruffy.
    b One – designer label of course.
    c Two – one for sport and one for casual wear
    d Can't remember – but they are all pink

11. **Which of the following would you most like to be?**
    a A successful career girl
    b A cat-walk model
    c A record-breaking sportswoman
    d A beautiful bride

ostly c's: Sporty Chic

ashion is not the most important thing in
ur life. You are energetic and enthusiastic
nd love to take on new challenges. You
ess for comfort and practicality and don't
ave the time for endless shopping trips.
o for it girl! Get the most out of life, but
hy not surprise everyone by looking
amorous once in a while!

Mostly d's: Girly Glamour

Just like Barbie, you love clothes, shopping
and the colour pink! You simply can't resist
anything with sparkles or frills, and
probably go wild for fake fur too! You are
good at putting outfits together and
co-ordinating your accessories. Glamour is
your middle name! Just remember not to try
too hard – less can sometimes be more!

You can... make it!

Chocolate Crunch

Teresa is having a sleepover for her birthday.
Barbie wants to make sweets to take to the party.
Here are the recipes she has chosen. You can try them too!

Ingredients:

25g butter
300g bar of milk chocolate
Breakfast cereal –
puffed rice or plain flakes
200g bar of white chocolate
Silver balls to decorate

1. Break up the bar of chocolate and melt in a saucepan with the butter.

2. Stir in enough breakfast cereal to bind together.

3. Spread mixture in a shallow glass dish and leave to cool.

4. Meanwhile break up white chocolate in a dish and melt over a saucepan of water.

5. Spread the melted white chocolate evenly over the cooled mixture.

6. Sprinkle with silver balls and when set, cut into squares.

Sugar Shoppe Truffles

Ingredients:

100g milk chocolate
275g sifted icing sugar
100g butter
Vanilla essence
Cocoa powder or chocolate sprinkles to finish

1. Break up the chocolate into a bowl and melt over a saucepan of water. Stir until there are no lumps left.

2. Mix in the butter until it melts.

4. When cool enough to handle, roll the mixture into small balls with your fingers.

3. Remove bowl from heat and stir in the icing sugar and vanilla essence.

5. Roll each truffle in cocoa powder or chocolate sprinkles and leave to set.

57

You can... make it!

A Sweet Surprise!

Turn your homemade sweets into special gifts, for birthdays, Christmas, or just for fun!

You will need:

Kitchen foil
White tissue paper
Coloured tissue paper
Curling ribbon

1. Wrap one or two sweets in kitchen foil to keep fresh.

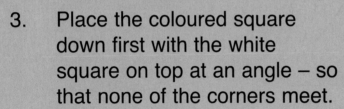

2. Cut 2 squares of tissue paper measuring 25cm x 25cm – one from your white tissue paper and one from your coloured tissue paper.

3. Place the coloured square down first with the white square on top at an angle – so that none of the corners meet.

4. Place your foil-wrapped sweet in the centre and scrunch the paper up around it.

5. Tie in place with curling ribbon and make a pretty bow.

58

"Tip: these work very well using pretty cellophane or net instead of tissue paper, and real ribbon instead of curling ribbon. They make lovely going-home gifts for parties."

How many wrapped-up sweeties can you count in total on this page?

You can... work it out!

4
2
3
5
6
7
8
9
1
54
55
11
53
12
13 15
52 51 47
14
50 49 45
46 44
48 43
40
42 16
41 17
39
38 25
36 27 18
30 26 19
34 28 21 20
32 23 22
29 24
31

59

"join the dots before
you start counting!"

Answer:

You can... colour it!

Barbie is preparing for a special night at the Theatre. Everyone will be wearing their most glamorous gowns and glittering jewels!

You can... colour it!

61

use your crayons and imagination
to give Barbie four different looks.
Then choose your favourite!

The Dream Dance

It was opening night at the ballet and the most glamorous ladies in Barbie Town swept along the red carpet into the Theatre. As they took their seats, the lights dimmed and the orchestra began to play…

Backstage, in her dressing room, Barbie stared into the mirror. She looked like a real ballerina in her pink tutu and satin shoes. But inside she felt so nervous.

"Come now, my dear," said Madame Lujenco, leading her into the wings. "This is what the hard work has been about. Go out on stage and enchant them with your beauty and grace. And remember the magic." She squeezed Barbie's hands tightly.

Barbie pulled herself up tall and straight, took a deep breath and pirouetted into the spotlight…

As the final note played Barbie curtseyed. The audience rose to its feet and the applause rang around the Theatre. Barbie held the fan in one hand and a giant bouquet in the other. She curtseyed again as flowers showered onto the stage. Up in the royal box, a shadowy figure leant over and threw down a single red rose. It landed at Barbie's feet, but when she looked back up, there was no one to be seen.

63

Barbie was a real star! Her dressing room was flooded with bouquets and cards and everyone wanted to see her. "You were wonderful!" they all said. "Simply magical!"

Just when she thought there was no one left to see, there was a knock at the door.

"Not more flowers!" said Christie, jumping up to answer it. The delivery boy handed her a bouquet of 24 red roses with a note attached. Christie read it out:

You dance like a prima ballerina. Please join me at the Chateau next Sunday 8pm.
D

"Oh, wow!" said Izzy.
"The Chateau!"
"Suddenly you have friends in high places!" said Kira.
"Who's D?" asked Ella.
"Oh gosh – what are you going to wear?!" said Teresa.

When she was finally alone, Barbie took the note and read it carefully. Something about it was familiar. "You dance like a prima ballerina," she said out loud. She had heard those words before. She hadn't told anyone about her dance with Danny. She wasn't sure if she had dreamed it. But there was his initial – D. "It couldn't be," she said to her reflection in the mirror. "Could it?"

64

The Dream Dance

The week passed in a whirl. Barbie danced every night, but every night when she looked up, the royal box was empty. Sunday came. Barbie had a new pink gown that she had been saving for a special occasion. She was almost ready when her friends called in.

"You look amazing!" said Kira. "Aren't you nervous?"

"Should I be?" asked Barbie.

"Well, who is this mysterious D?" said Ella. "You've never even met him!"

"I've heard the people at the Chateau are very grand!" said Teresa.

"He might be an Italian Count!" breathed Izzy.

"Stop!" said Barbie. "You're making me nervous! I'll tell you all about it tomorrow!"

Barbie settled into the back of the taxi. She was really quite calm. It was as if this was what she had been waiting for. As if it was meant to be.

65

The Chateau stood on the hill outside Barbie Town. As Barbie stepped out at the splendid gates she could hear music playing. It was a party. There were people in the gardens and the sound of laughter drifted out from the brightly lit rooms. Barbie followed the music to a grand ballroom. She stood in the doorway, and searched the room for the tall figure and handsome face that had swept her off her feet that night at the Ballet Studio. Then suddenly someone was at her side.

"You're here! I'm so happy! You danced so beautifully on stage, I wanted to thank you. Please, enjoy my party!"

Barbie stared at the elegant woman who was standing next to her.

"Excuse my manners. I am Countess Daniella Sentigella. Welcome to my home."

"But…" Barbie stammered. "But… D… stands for Daniella?! I wasn't… I mean, I'm sorry, I'm not feeling well, please excuse me!" And she ran through the French doors and out into the moonlit garden.

66

Here she stopped and caught her breath. She felt so disappointed – and foolish. She had really believed that Danny would be there. Perhaps he was only a dream. Now she just wanted to go home.

She had almost reached the gate when she heard footsteps running behind her. She turned and looked back. There, silhouetted against the bright lights was the tall figure she had been longing to see.

Danny ran up to her and took her hand.

"You're here!" she whispered. "You're real!"

"I only just arrived," he began. "I've been dancing in Rome. But I'm here now. You already met my mother? I knew it was you when she told me she had been to the ballet and invited the most beautiful ballerina to the party!"

Then a voice called from inside: "Daniel! Come in, and bring your beautiful princess with you. Everyone is waiting to see you both dance!"

He took her hand and they walked back towards the Chateau.

And that night, over Barbie Town, the stars twinkled with a special kind of magic.

You can... discover it!

Discover Your Dream!

What do you dream of? Find out with this fun flow-quiz. Simply answer yes or no to each question and see where the arrows take you!

Do you enjoy performing on stage?
— Yes / No

Are you a good dancer?
— Yes / No

Do you believe in love at first sight?
— Yes / No

Do you have ballet shoes?
— No

Do you like having your photo taken?
— No

Do you like wearing long, floaty dresses?
— No

Do you like being waited on?
— Yes

Yes / Yes / Yes / No / Yes

Are you very graceful?
— No

Do you know the words to lots of pop songs?
— No

Is white your favourite colour?
— No

Do you like wearing jewellery?

Yes / Yes / Yes / No / Yes

Do you have a tutu?
— No

Are you a bit of a show-off?
— No

Do you know how many bridesmaids you want?
— No

Do you believe in magic?

Yes / Yes / Yes / No / Yes

A graceful ballerina!

You want to dance on stage and delight the audience with your charm and beauty. You only have to work hard and your dream may come true!

The star of the show!

Cue bright lights and action! You have arrived and intend to sing, dance or act your way into the limelight! You dream of fame and fortune. Here's hoping your big break comes soon!

A beautiful bride!

You are in love with being in love! You long for romance and can't wait to walk down the aisle in your white gown under a shower of confetti!

A glittering princess!

You can see yourself living in castle, with servants to wait o you and beautifu dresses and jewe to wear. All you need now is you handsome prince

Make my dream come true...

"Now everything is perfect for my special day."

69

Barbie Magazine

Packed with
● Stories ● Colouring ● Puzzles ● Fashion ● Make-its ● Posters

FREE Hair Clips!

Barbie™

Fashion & Friends

Win a Barbie as Sleeping Beauty Doll!

FREE Hair Clips!

Issue No. 82

If your Free Gift is missing from here, please tell your newsagent.

Read Barbie's Ballet Secrets!

Only £1.50 Fantastic free gift with every issue!

70

Barbie™ On sale every 3 weeks in all good supermarkets and newsagents!